Tom Sawyer

Based on stories from
The Adventures of Tom Sawyer **by Mark Twain**

Michael Leviton

SCHOLASTIC INC.
New York Toronto London Auckland Sydney
Mexico City New Delhi Hong Kong Buenos Aires

**Illustrations
Glin Dibley**

Text copyright © 2004 by Scholastic Inc.
Illustrations copyright © 2004 by Glin Dibley.
All rights reserved. Published by Scholastic Inc.
Printed in the U.S.A.

ISBN 0-439-68251-7

8   9   10   23   12 11

Contents

Tom Sawyer's day of fun is ruined.
He has to spend all day painting the fence!

The Fence

It was summer, and the world was bright. Everyone was happy, except for Tom Sawyer.

Tom sat on the sidewalk with a bucket of paint and a paintbrush. He looked up at a huge fence 30 yards long and nine feet high. He had to paint the whole thing.

Tom lived with his Aunt Polly. She always gave him lots of **chores**. Today,

chores jobs

The fence was huge—and Tom had to paint the whole thing himself.

she was making him paint her fence. Aunt Polly didn't care that summer was the best season of the year. She didn't care that Saturday was the best day of the week.

Tom sighed, dipped the brush in the paint, and painted one board. Then he looked at the hundreds of boards he still had left to paint. "What a rotten world!" he said. "I can't believe I have to work on a sunny day like this!"

Tom knew that soon his friends would pass by on their way to some great **adventure**. They would laugh at him for having to work. That made him even angrier.

Then Tom had an idea. He'd try to pay

---

adventure an exciting or dangerous experience

another kid to paint for him! He dug in his pockets, looking for change. But he found only two marbles and a piece of trash. This was not enough to pay anyone to do anything, so he put the stuff back in his pockets.

Then Tom Sawyer had another idea.

Tom's Trick

A few minutes later, Tom saw his friend Ben walking down the street. Tom knew Ben would stop to make fun of him—so Ben would be his first **victim**!

Ben was making train noises, and eating an apple. Tom pretended not to notice Ben, and he pretended not to hear when Ben laughed and said, "So, Tom

victim a person treated badly or tricked

Sawyer has work to do! Poor baby!"

Ben stepped closer. The smell of Ben's apple was making Tom hungry.

Ben said, "Hey, Tom, today is going to be the best day of the year. It's really a shame you'll have to miss it!"

Then, Tom turned and acted surprised. He said, "Ben! I didn't see you there!"

"I'm going swimming," Ben said. "Too bad you have to work! Ha ha! Have fun painting the fence!"

Tom acted **confused**. He said, "What do you mean—I have to work?"

Now Ben looked confused. "You're painting, aren't you? Isn't that work?"

Tom said, "Maybe it is, and maybe it isn't. But I like it better than swimming."

confused not understanding

Ben was confused. "Wait a minute! You *like* painting?" he asked Tom.

"Wait a minute!" Ben said. "Are you telling me that you *like* painting?"

Tom started to paint again. "It's not every day that a boy gets to paint a fence," he said.

Ben stopped eating his apple. He watched Tom paint for a while and then said, "Hey, Tom, may I paint a little?"

Tom laughed inside, but he held back his smile. "Aunt Polly doesn't let just any kid paint her fence! Only I can do it."

"Come on, Tom," Ben said. "I can do it! Just let me try! If I had a fence to paint, I'd let *you* help!"

Tom Makes a Deal

"It's not up to me," Tom said seriously. "Aunt Polly makes the rules."

"I'll give you half my apple," Ben said.

"Well, okay," Tom said. He started to give Ben the brush, but then he pulled it away at the last minute. Tom held the brush tightly and said, "I'm sorry Ben. I really can't."

"Okay, Tom, I'll give you *all* of the apple," Ben said.

Tom was laughing inside as he handed Ben the brush.

Ben worked, sweating in the sun. Tom sat in the shade and ate his apple.

Every now and then, another boy walked by. The boys always stopped to laugh, but in the end, they always begged Tom to let them help with the painting.

When Ben got tired, Billy wanted a turn. Billy gave Tom his kite. Then, when Billy's time was up, Johnny begged Tom for a chance to paint. Johnny gave Tom a dead rat on a string and showed him how to swing it. This **swapping** went

swapping trading

"Maybe the world is not so bad after all," Tom said to himself.

on for hours.

By two o'clock, Tom had all kinds of great stuff. He had a piece of chalk and two tadpoles. He had a key that wouldn't unlock anything. He had six firecrackers and a knife-handle. He had a dog collar—but no dog.

The fence now had three coats of paint on it, and all the kids agreed: It had been the best day of the summer.

Tom said to himself, "Maybe the world is not so bad after all."

Work or Play?

Tom had learned that people want things they can't have. So, if you want to make people want something, you should make it hard to get!

Tom should also have learned that "work" is what you call something you have to do. "Play" is what you don't have to do. For example, digging is work if your mother makes you dig for moles, but if you dig to reach China, that's fun!

Tom thought about the **fortune** he had made that day. Then, he went back inside to find Aunt Polly. He couldn't wait to show her the fence.

Do you think you would have been tricked by Tom Sawyer? Why or why not?

fortune lots of money or valuable things

You don't get to see your own funeral—unless you're Tom Sawyer!

Tom's Funeral

"Tom Sawyer, you are a cheater and a liar!" Becky Thatcher shouted. "Our **engagement** is off!"

"But Becky," Tom said. "Why?"

"Because I just found out that you asked *Sally* to marry you only last week!"

"Sure, I used to be in love with Sally," Tom said. "But now I'm in love with you! Look, I even brought you a doorknob as a wedding present!" He held out a

engagement a plan to get married

"I deserve a diamond ring, not a dirty old doorknob!" Becky said.

doorknob he had found in the trash.

"I deserve a diamond ring, not a dirty old doorknob!" Becky shouted. "Tom Sawyer, I wish you were dead!"

Pirates on Devil's Island

Tom walked through town looking for his friends Huck and Ben. Tom knew they could help him forget about Becky.

When he found them he said, "Hey guys, let's take a raft and sail to Devil's Island and be pirates!"

The boys put patches on their eyes and found a rag in the trash to use as their flag. They made ten sandwiches each so they wouldn't starve on the island.

Devil's Island was in the middle of a

lake. The people who lived near this lake always left their rafts on the shore. So, the gang of pirates just took one and sailed to Devil's Island.

They spent the day digging holes in the ground, looking for treasure. As the sun started to go down and it got colder, they decided to go home.

Tom and his friends spent the day digging for treasure.

But when they went to get their raft, they saw that it was gone.

"It must have **drifted** off," Ben said.

"We'll have to wait here till we're **rescued**," Huck said.

So, they slept on the ground with rocks as pillows. "I hate being a pirate," Tom said.

"Tom Was Such a Good Boy!"

The next morning, a boat came to Devil's Island to dump trash. Tom asked the captain for a ride back to shore. But there was only one extra seat in the boat.

Tom said to Huck and Ben, "I'll go back to shore. Then I'll come get you later with another raft."

drifted moved wherever the water or wind took it

rescued saved

When the trash boat reached shore, Tom decided to stop by his Aunt Polly's house for a piece of pie. When he got there, he saw that there were black sheets over the windows. Through the back door, he heard Aunt Polly crying! He listened from outside.

Aunt Polly said, "Are you sure Tom is dead?"

A man said, "We found their raft. Those boys drowned in the lake. I'm sorry. We should have a **funeral** for them tomorrow."

Aunt Polly started to cry harder. She said, "Tom was such a good boy! I shouldn't have always yelled at him and given him so many chores!"

funeral an event held when someone dies

Tom laughed to himself. "What good luck! Everyone thinks we're dead!"

Tom went back to the lake. He took another raft and headed to Devil's Island. He couldn't wait to tell Huck and Ben the news.

"Our funeral is tomorrow," Tom told them. "Let's go see it!"

Tom's Funeral

The boys slept on the island another night. Then, they set sail early the next morning so they'd get to church before anyone else. They climbed up to the church's ceiling and sat on the **rafters**. No one could see them up there.

They waited until people started to

rafters wooden boards near the ceiling that help support the building

arrive. Tom saw Becky walk in and sit down with a group of her friends. She was very upset. "I've lost my husband!" she cried.

Another girl said, "Tom wasn't your husband. You told Tom you wished he was dead!"

"No, I didn't!" Becky shouted. "I would never say that to a boy as sweet as Tom Sawyer!" Then she started to speak sadly to herself again. "I wish I had taken that lovely doorknob he tried to give me."

Tom was ready to die of laughter!

Becky went on, "I was the last person to see Tom alive."

"No, you weren't," another girl said.

Becky Thatcher was very upset. "I've lost my husband!" she cried.

"I saw him last!"

"No, I did!" a boy shouted.

They kept fighting about who had seen Tom last until one boy interrupted them. He cleared his throat and said proudly, "Tom Sawyer tricked me once!"

The other boys laughed. "That's no big deal," one said. "Everyone here has been tricked by Tom Sawyer!"

The Last Laugh

Soon, the funeral began. Aunt Polly walked into church wearing all black, crying her eyes out.

Ben turned to Tom. "Don't you feel a little guilty?" Ben asked.

"Are you kidding?" Tom said. "This is

the most fun I've ever had!"

The **preacher** gave a **sermon** about the boys. "Sure, they seemed to be bad boys. But they were really the best boys in town!"

Tom, Huck, and Ben were laughing so hard that they could barely hold onto the rafters. Tom whispered to Huck and Ben, "Now it's time for us to surprise them!"

The boys climbed quietly down from the rafters. When they reached the floor, they all ran up the center **aisle**, up to the platform where the preacher stood. They smiled and bowed and Tom said, "Ha ha! We're alive! We fooled all of you! Ha ha!"

Huck and Ben joined in shouting, "Ha

preacher a religious leader
sermon a speech given during a religious service
aisle a passage that runs between rows of seats in a theater, church or other building

"Ha ha! We're alive! We fooled all of you!" Tom said.

ha! We tricked you! Ha ha!"

Becky Thatcher stood up and yelled, "Tom Sawyer, you're the meanest boy in the whole world! I hate you!"

"Ha ha!" Tom said. "That's not what you said a minute ago!"

"You weren't supposed to hear that!" she said. "Besides, I was lying!"

Just then Aunt Polly interrupted. With tears in her eyes, she ran up and hugged Tom. "I'm so glad you're alive!" she cried.

Tom felt warm inside. It was nice to know how much everyone loved him.

"I'm so glad you're alive," Aunt Polly said again, "Because that means I can kill you!"

Polly stopped hugging Tom, grabbed his ear, and pulled him home where she explained that he would be **grounded** for the rest of his life and that she would give him so many chores that he would probably die of hard work. But the whole time Aunt Polly shouted, Tom was laughing. It had all been worth it!

What did the town think of Tom when they thought he was dead? What do they think of Tom when they find out he's not dead?

grounded not allowed to leave the house

Glossary

adventure *(noun)* an exciting or dangerous experience

aisle *(noun)* a passage that runs between rows of seats in a theater, church, or other building

chores *(noun)* jobs

confused *(adjective)* not understanding *(related words: confuse, confusion)*

drifted *(verb)* moved wherever the water or wind took it *(related word: drift)*

engagement *(noun)* a plan to get married

fortune *(noun)* lots of money or valuable things

funeral *(noun)* an event held when someone dies

grounded *(adjective)* not allowed to leave the house

preacher *(noun)* a religious leader *(related word: preach)*

rafters *(noun)* wooden boards near the ceiling that help support the building

rescued *(verb)* saved

sermon *(noun)* a speech given during a religious service

swapping *(noun)* trading *(related word: swap)*

victim *(noun)* a person treated badly or tricked